Spelling Journal

A Student-Created Reference

by Denise Eide

LogicofEnglish®

PEDIALEARNING
INCORPORATED

Spelling Journal

Pedia Learning Inc.
10800 Lyndale Ave S. Suite 181
Minneapolis, MN 55420

Cover Images: Cienpies Design & Communication, Shutterstock

ISBN 978-1-936706-67-9

Second Edition

10 9 8 7 6 5 4 3 2

www.LogicOfEnglish.com

Table of Contents

What is a Spelling Journal?

The trickiest English words to spell include sounds that can be spelled in multiple ways. For example, /ā/ can be spelled **ai** as in pl**ai**n, **ay** as in w**ay**, **ea** as in gr**ea**t, or five other spellings. A Spelling Journal provides a system for collecting, categorizing, and analyzing these troublesome words so they can be understood and mastered.

How Does It Work?

The Spelling Journal is organized first by sounds, and then by spellings. The gray box in the top corner of each page represents the sound. The Sound to Spelling Reference on the following page can help you locate the sound you're looking for. Once you've found the sound, look at the letters across the top of each column to find a specific spelling. Most spellings have additional hints beneath them to guide you in their use. In each column, write words represented by that spelling. The Spelling Journal is also an excellent place to collect words you frequently misspell and words with infrequent spellings. Highlight the spelling of the targeted sound or write it in red. The Spelling Journal can be used as a personal reference tool when you write.

Write words that use ea to spell /ē/. Examples: eat, seat

Why Should I Use It?

Using a Spelling Journal can help you:
- Discover which phonograms and spelling rules are most commonly used.
- Learn which phonograms and rules are infrequently used.
- Narrow memorization to the sounds which have multiple options for spelling.
- More clearly understand your options for spelling a given sound.
- Mentally organize your knowledge about words.

Key

_a, _e, _i, _o, _u, _y
A syllable ending with a single vowel. Spelling Rules 4 and 5.

i_ _, o_ _
I or O followed by two consonants. Spelling Rule 8.

a_e, e_e, i_e, o_e, u_e, y_e
The vowel says its long sound because of the silent final E. Spelling Rule 12.

ce, ci, cy
C followed by an E, I, or Y. Spelling Rule 1.

ge, gi, gy
G followed by an E, I, or Y. Spelling Rule 2.

Sound to Spelling Reference

The sounds highlighted in gray have only one spelling or include a form of the past tense phonogram ED. Since these pose no difficulty for spelling, they are not included in the Spelling Journal.

Page	Sound	Sample Words
	ă	mat
8	ā	apron, late, laid, play, steak, their, they, eight
12	ä	father, author, taught, saw
14	b	bat, buy
	d	dad, pulled
15	ě	wet, bread
16	ē	be, eve, eat, tree, protein, key, medium, piece, baby
21	f	foot, phone
22	g	big, guide, get, gift, foggy
	h	hat
25	ǐ	it, gym
26	ī	ivy, by, night, slide, type, blind, feisty, height
30	j	job, gem, rigid, gym, edge
33	k	cat, kit, school, back
	l	lap
	m	me
35	n	nut, gnat, know
37	ǒ	on, thought
38	ō	go, smoke, cold, coat, toe, floor, soul, snow, though
43	ö	do, food, flew, group, tuna, flute, fruit, shoe, through
	p	pan
	qu	queen
48	r	ran, write
49	s	sent, cent, circle, cycle
	t	tip, picked

Page	Sound	Sample Words
51	ǔ	up, country
52	ū	unit, cute, few
54	ü	put, took
	v	van
55	w	wall, whisper
	ks	fox
56	y	yard, onion
57	z	as, zip
	är	car
58	ch	child, butcher
	ĕd	traded
59	er	her, bird, hurt, search
	ng	sing
61	oi	boil, boy
	or	lord
62	ow	house, plow, bough
64	sh	she, chef, nation, session, spacious
	th	thin
	TH	this
	wer	work
	wh	whisper
	zh	division
67	sē	receive
67	ăf	laugh
68	ŏf	trough
68	ŭf	rough
69	ə	other, about, the

Phonogram Table

The sounds for each phonogram are listed in order of frequency.

Sound		Sample Words			
a	/ă-ā-ä/	mat	table	father	
ai	/ā/	laid			
ar	/är/	car			
au	/ä/	author			
augh	/ä-ăf/	taught	laugh		
aw	/ä/	saw			
ay	/ā/	play			
b	/b/	bat			
bu	/b/	buy			
c	/k-s/	cat	cent		
cei	/sē/	receive			
ch	/ch-k-sh/	child	school	chef	
ci	/sh/	spacious			
ck	/k/	back			
d	/d/	dad			
dge	/j/	edge			
e	/ĕ-ē/	tent	be		
ea	/ē-ĕ-ā/	eat	bread	steak	
ear	/er/	search			
ed	/ed-d-t/	traded	pulled	picked	
ee	/ē/	tree			
ei	/ā-ē-ī/	their	protein	feisty	
eigh	/ā-ī/	eight	height		
er	/er/	her			
ew	/ö-ū/	flew	few		
ey	/ā-ē/	they	key		
f	/f/	foot			
g	/g-j/	big	gym		
gn	/n/	sign			
gu	/g-gw/	guide	language		
h	/h/	hat			
i	/ĭ-ī-ē-y/	it	ivy	stadium onion	
ie	/ē/	field			
igh	/ī/	night			
ir	/er/	bird			
j	/j/	job			
k	/k/	kit			
kn	/n/	know			

Sound		Sample Words			
l	/l/	lap			
m	/m/	me			
n	/n/	nut			
ng	/ng/	sing			
o	/ŏ-ō-ö/	on	go	do	
oa	/ō/	coat			
oe	/ō-ö/	toe	shoe		
oi	/oi/	boil			
oo	/ö-ü-ō/	food	took	floor	
or	/or/	lord			
ou	/ow-ō-ö-ŭ/	house	soul	group	country
ough	/ŏ-ō-ö-ow-ŭf-ŏf/	thought though through bough rough trough			
ow	/ow-ō/	plow	snow		
oy	/oi/	boy			
p	/p/	pan			
ph	/f/	phone			
qu	/qu/	queen			
r	/r/	ran			
s	/s-z/	sent	as		
sh	/sh/	she			
si	/sh-zh/	session	division		
t	/t/	tip			
tch	/ch/	butcher			
th	/th-TH/	thin	this		
ti	/sh/	partial			
u	/ŭ-ū-ö-ü/	up	pupil	flute	put
ui	/ö/	fruit			
ur	/er/	hurts			
v	/v/	van			
w	/w/	wall			
wh	/wh/	whisper			
wor	/wer/	worm			
wr	/r/	write			
x	/ks/	fox			
y	/y-ĭ-ī-ē/	yard	gym	by	baby
z	/z/	zip			

Spelling Rules

1. C always softens to /s/ when followed by E, I, or Y. Otherwise, C says /k/.
2. G may soften to /j/ only when followed by E, I, or Y. Otherwise, G says /g/.
3. English words do not end in I, U, V, or J.
4. A E O U usually say their names at the end of a syllable.
5. I and Y may say /ĭ/ or /ī/ at the end of a syllable.
6. When a one-syllable word ends in a single vowel Y, it says /ī/.
7. Y says /ē/ **only** at the end of a multi-syllable word. I says /ē/ at the end of a syllable that is followed by a vowel and at the end of foreign words.
8. I and O may say /ī/ and /ō/ when followed by two consonants.
9. AY usually spells the sound /ā/ at the end of a base word.
10. When a word ends with the phonogram A, it says /ä/. A may also say /ä/ after a W or before an L.
11. Q always needs a U; therefore, U is not a vowel here.
12. Silent Final E Rules

    12.1 The vowel says its name because of the E.

    12.2 English words do not end in V or U.

    12.3 The C says /s/ and the G says /j/ because of the E.

    12.4 Every syllable must have a written vowel.

    12.5 Add an E to keep singular words that end in the letter S from looking plural.

    12.6 Add an E to make the word look bigger.

    12.7 TH says its voiced sound /TH/ because of the E.

    12.8 Add an E to clarify meaning.

    12.9 Unseen reason.

13. Drop the silent final E when adding a vowel suffix only if it is allowed by other spelling rules.
14. Double the last consonant when adding a vowel suffix to words ending in **one** vowel followed by **one** consonant only if the syllable before the suffix is stressed.* 　　*This is always true for one-syllable words.
15. Single vowel Y changes to I when adding any ending, unless the ending begins with I.
16. Two I's cannot be next to one another in English words.
17. TI, CI, and SI are used only at the beginning of any syllable after the first one.
18. SH spells /sh/ at the beginning of a base word and at the end of the syllable. SH never spells /sh/ at the beginning of any syllable after the first one, except for the ending -*ship*.
19. To make a verb past tense, add the ending -ED unless it is an irregular verb.
20. -ED, past tense ending, forms another syllable when the base word ends in /d/ or /t/. Otherwise, -ED says /d/ or /t/.
21. To make a noun plural, add the ending -S, unless the word hisses or changes; then add -ES. Some nouns have no change or an irregular spelling.
22. To make a verb 3rd person singular, add the ending -S, unless the word hisses or changes; then add -ES. Only four verbs are irregular.
23. AL- is a prefix written with one L when preceding another syllable.
24. -FUL is a suffix written with one L when added to another syllable.
25. DGE is used only after a single vowel which says its short sound.
26. CK is used only after a single vowel which says its short sound.
27. TCH is used only after a single vowel which says its short or broad sound.
28. AUGH, EIGH, IGH, OUGH. Phonograms ending in GH are used only at the end of a base word or before the letter T. The GH is either silent or pronounced /f/.
29. Z, never S, spells /z/ at the beginning of a base word.
30. We often double F, L, and S after a single, short or broad vowel at the end of a base word. Occasionally other letters also are doubled.
31. Any vowel may say one of the schwa sounds, /ŭ/ or /ĭ/, in an unstressed syllable or unstressed word. O may also say /ŭ/ in a stressed syllable next to a W, TH, M, N, or V.

ā

_a

Used at the end of the syllable
in the middle of the word.

a_e

Used in the middle of the syllable.

ai

May NOT be used at the end of English words. Used in the middle of the syllable.

ay

Used at the end of the base word.

ā

ea

9 words
Used in the middle of the syllable.

ei

May NOT be used at the end of English
words. Used in the middle of the syllable.

_____

_____

_____

_____

_____

_____

_____

_____

_____

_____

_____

_____

_____

_____

ey

10 words
Used at the end of the base word.

eigh

5 words
Used at the end of the word or before a T.

_____

_____

_____

_____

_____

_____

_____

_____

_____

_____

_____

_____

ä

a

Most commonly used at the end of the word, after a W, or before an L.

au

May NOT be used at the end of English words. Used in the middle of the syllable.

augh

9 words

Used at the end of the word or before a T.

aw

Most commonly used at the
end of the word.

b

bu

Used at the beginning of the base word.

e

Used in the middle of the syllable.

ea

Used in the middle of the syllable.

_e

Used at the end of the syllable.

e_e

Used in the middle of the syllable.

16

ea

Used at the beginning of the word, and both
in the middle and at the end of the syllable.

ee

Used both in the middle and
at the end of the syllable.

ei

13 words
Used in the middle of the syllable.

ey

10 words
Used at the end of the syllable.

i

Latin Roots
Used at the end of the syllable before another vowel. Used at the end of foreign words.

_____

_____

_____

_____

_____

_____

_____

_____

_____

_____

_____

_____

_____

_____

ie

Used in the middle and at the end of the syllable.

_____

_____

_____

_____

_____

_____

_____

_____

_____

_____

_____

_____

_____

_____

ē

y

Used at the end of
multi-syllable base words.

f

ph

Greek Roots

g

g

gu

ge

Hard /g/ before an E.

gi

Hard /g/ before an I.

g

gy

Hard /g/ before a Y.

i

Used in the middle of the syllable
and at the end of the syllable.

y

Latin and Greek Roots
Used in the middle of the syllable
and at the end of the syllable.

i

_i

Used at the end of the syllable.

_y

Most commonly used at the end of a one-syllable word. Also used at the end of the syllable in the middle of the word.

_____   _____

_____   _____

_____   _____

_____   _____

_____   _____

_____   _____

_____   _____

_____   _____

_____   _____

_____   _____

_____   _____

_____   _____

_____   _____

_____   _____

i_e

Used in the middle of the syllable.

y_e

Used in the middle of the syllable.

i__ _

Long /ī/ before two consonants.

_igh

19 words
Used at the end of the word or before a T.

ei

23 words

eigh

2 words
Used at the end of the word or before a T.

j

ge

Soft /j/ before an E.

g

Soft /j/ before an I.

g

Soft /j/ before a Y.

dge

Used only after a
single, short vowel.

c

Used before an A, O, U, and before a consonant. Also used at the end of the word.

k

Most commonly used before an E, I, or Y. Used at the end of the word.

ck

Used only after a
single, short vowel.

ch

Greek Roots

n

gn

Used both at the beginning
and the end of a base word.

kn

Used only at the beginning
of a base word.

o

Used in the middle of the syllable.

ough

8 words
Used at the end of the word or before a T.

ō

_o

Used at the end of the syllable.

o_e

Used in the middle of the syllable.

38

o_ _

Long /ō/ before two consonants.

oa

Used in the middle of the syllable.

ō

ou

Used in the middle of the syllable.

ow

Most commonly used
at the end of the base word.

ough

5 words
Used at the end of the word or before a T.

oo

3 words
Used in the middle of the syllable.

oe

9 words
Used at the end of short words.

o   oo

ew

Most commonly used at the
end of a base word.

ou

Used in the middle of the syllable.

_u

Used at the end of the syllable.

u_e

Used in the middle of the syllable.

ui

7 words
Used in the middle of the syllable.

oe

2 words

ough

1 word

r

wr

Used at the beginning of a base word.

s

ce

Soft /s/ before an E.

S

ci

Soft /s/ before an I.

cy

Soft /s/ before a Y.

u

Used in the middle of the syllable.

ou

May NOT be used at the end of English words. Used in the middle of the syllable.

_____

_____

_____

_____

_____

_____

_____

_____

_____

_____

_____

_____

_____

_____

_u

Used at the end of the syllable.

u_e

Used in the middle of the syllable.

ew

Most commonly used at the
end of a base word.

u

Used in the middle of the syllable.

oo

22 words
Most commonly used in 4-5 letter words.

w

wh

Used at the beginning
of the base word.

y

Used at the beginning of the word.

i

Never used to spell /y/ at the beginning of the word.

_____

_____

_____

_____

_____

_____

_____

_____

_____

_____

_____

_____

_____

_____

Z

Always used to spell /z/ at the beginning of the word. Also used in the middle and at the end of the word.

S

Most common spelling of /z/, but never at the beginning of the word.

Z

ch

tch

Used only after a single, short or broad vowel.

er

Most common spelling of /er/.

ir

ur

ear

13 words

oi

May NOT be used at the end of the word.

oy

May be used at the end of the word.

ou

May NOT be used at
the end of English words.

ow

May be used both in the middle
and at the end of the word.

62

ough

3 words

Used at the end of the word or before a T.

sh

sh

Used at the beginning
of the word, at the end of the
syllable, and in the ending *-ship*.

ch

French Loan Words

_____   _____

_____   _____

_____   _____

_____   _____

_____   _____

_____   _____

_____   _____

_____   _____

_____   _____

_____   _____

_____   _____

_____   _____

_____   _____

_____   _____

_____   _____

ti

Latin Roots
Used only at the beginning of
a syllable after the first one.

_____

_____

_____

_____

_____

_____

_____

_____

_____

_____

_____

_____

_____

si

Latin Roots
Used only at the beginning of
a syllable after the first one.

_____

_____

_____

_____

_____

_____

_____

_____

_____

_____

_____

_____

_____

ci

Latin Roots
Used only at the beginning of
a syllable after the first one.

cei

8 words

 augh

2 words
Used at the end of the word or before a T.

 ough

2 words

Used at the end of the word or before a T.

 ough

3 words

Used at the end of the word or before a T.

68

Lazy O

Before V, TH, M, or N. After W.

Unstressed Syllable

Any vowel saying its schwa sound in an unstressed syllable.

Unstressed Word

A small grammatical word where the vowel says its schwa sound when
the word is unstressed in a sentence. For example: a, the, was.

_____   _____

_____   _____

_____   _____

_____   _____

_____   _____

_____   _____

_____   _____

_____   _____

_____   _____

_____   _____

_____   _____

_____   _____

_____   _____